Happy Birthday
Love to Finley From !
2020

Home Sweet Home, where it all began in 1991.

An ODE to Flight, Life, and LOVE

Each of us has a child inside. A Little Magic. A child born Innocent and ready to Smile. Circumstance shortens our childhood, or extends it. Yet in each of us remains the memory of our Innocence. This story is dedicated to that sweet child and the purity of those moments when we began our journey to adulthood, learning the ways and whims of
a world which we inherited.

This book is two tales in one. It may be read as a children's book simply by using the photos, inviting the reader to tell their *own* ~ *actually,* a lot of fun. In the second book, Little Magic, older, tells *his* story using the Logbook of *his* personal journey beside each photo.

LOVE is a gift. Life is a journey.

Cover design and Images by Rod Magner

ISBN 9780996157247

littlemagic.com Email: alittlemagic@gmail.com

LITTLE MAGIC

JUST IMAGINE

Little Magic

THE "LITTLE MAGIC" LOGBOOK

We are friends. Really good friends. He made me out of plywood and conduit and aluminum. Even PVC pipe ends for my engine, and a yellow button on my control stick. He painted me like the big biplane he flew. He gave me three coats of paint and polished me and gave me a name, Little Magic.

When I was completed in the tiny workshop down by the water, he was very anxious to get me to the hangar and show me off. In his heart, he was a child again whenever he watched children pedal me around the hangar floor. I watched him come and go all summer long in Magic One, the elephant ear TravelAir in which he flew scenic rides. I sat in the quiet of the hangar that first summer waiting for him to return so I could listen to the people tell him how beautiful flying in the open air was and how the wind seemed to clear the cobwebs from their vision.

Many evenings we sat together in the old hangar, watching the sun set, slimming gold leaf to wrinkly black night. We marked the passage of these moments with good feelings, a sense of timelessness swirling in our midst. Though there were wars in far off places, here, in the cooling hangar, there was merely silence. A promise that tomorrow would yield more of the wonderful same.

Not all promises are kept. Not all tomorrows are met. No two clouds are the same… I am Little Magic, and I wish to see for myself, more than anything else, the world beyond my hangar. I am just a pedal plane. Mobile, inanimate, a slave to the muscle energy of children, smiling with delight. When the hangar doors close and my pilot goes home, I am already home. Left behind a bit like a rundown watch.

I decided finally, that whatever laws of physics demanded my role as a quiet little pedal plane, doomed to making circles on the hangar floor and occasionally down main street in the big parade...whatever those laws were, they would have to bend. The laws of physics are really never broken, merely superceded. I knew this, sure as light bent through raindrops makes rainbows. I wanted to surf on the old principles as far as they could fly me. To an edge of quantum uncertainty. From there I wanted to see the landscape of all possibilities. To look in wonder and touch eternity. To Learn, I would start on Orcas Island!

After 16 years living in a hangar, where do pedal planes get such frivolous dreams?

I will tell you it is not from listening to adults on the home shopping channel. Or from teenagers in love. Or even to the lofty buzz of important cell phones.

I heard it from the heart of the first child that discovered me parked in the corner of the hangar. There was no illusion of self-importance in her desire which commanded me to move in concert with her wishes. The emotion closest to perfection in it was simply Joy, unencumbered by direction, goal, purpose or intent. The eyes of adults saw 'cute' and 'darling' which were word-masks for concealing something; the brilliant edge of trust and innocence they long ago lost... But an ember in each of them bursts into flame with the oxygen of that memory, though it is usually lost again in the immediate wind of daily living. Almost in fact with the very next breath. Yet I see it clearly. I would search for the child in every adult, airplane or human, that tiny window into the soul of the world, where all of the good just IS and the bad slips unerringly away.

The strangest law to me in all of physics is "growing up." Actually no one has ever written the law down. Everyone simply follows it. There are numerous little side laws that are written down, about the arrow of time for instance, and the distances between things, even unseen things. "Growing *UP,*" is a given, an inescapable conclusion. Photographs show blurry water when exposed for more than a fraction of a second. A person's photographic history runs from baby pictures to gray hair and wrinkled skin. My skin is not wrinkled yet but I have heard people in the hangar discuss "past lives" and sometimes I've sensed one in me. So it was in the law of growing up that I wished to pan for gold. To sail for a distant shore, flex my own wings. To really FLY on my tiny but sturdy yellow wings of plywood.

I heard laughter in the cosmos the first time I even thought the idea. I learned to call it the Cosmic Chuckle. There are particles in atomic physics which move whenever their twin moves, separated across vast expanses in space-time. The Cosmic Chuckle is like that. Think a crazy idea, you hear the laughter. I chose to hurl myself in the direction of the laughter, searching, never wishing to grow up. To locate the source of the *first* cosmic chuckle. And that sweet child in every adult.

I call her mother, Magic One. We talk a lot. I told her my idea and there was no hesitation. She smiled and wished me well. Airplanes, especially biplanes I believe, have been tuned to hear the music of the universe in ways yet to be revealed. And so it was I occasionally left the comfort of my old hangar home and explored my island and, I confess, a little beyond. I knew my mother's ways, and I was patient, though anxious, to be on MY way. My first venture beyond the hangar I called home.

Just Imagine, I thought, no more boredom, or fear, I can learn to navigate reality!

"Listen and watch Little Magic, and you will learn things I cannot teach," she said.

"Deal Mom!" I smiled.

"And be home before sunset. Remember, you have no navigation lights yet!"

Mothers are like that

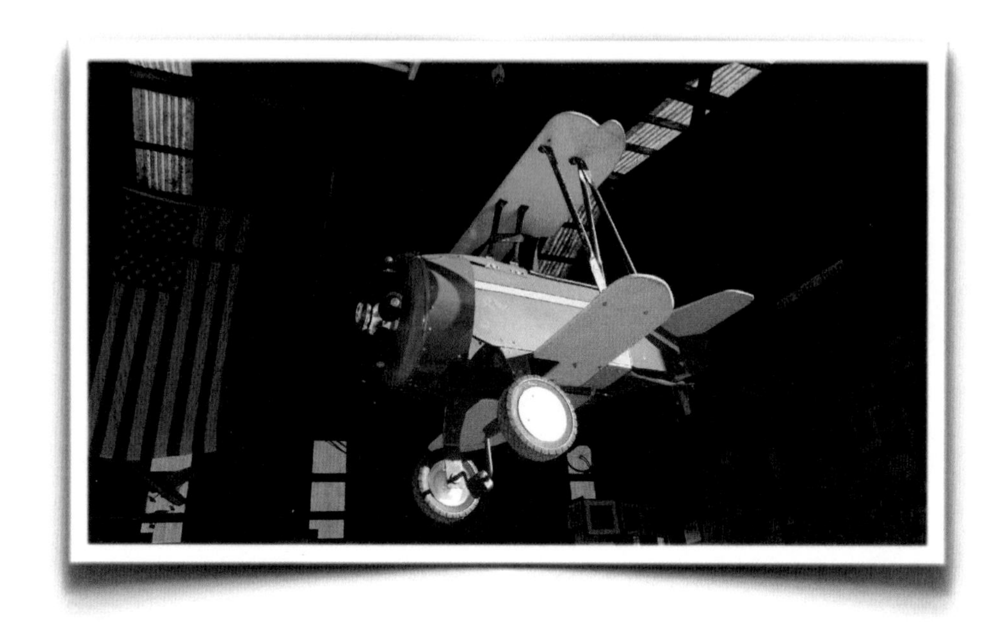

PRACTICE PRACTICE

Flying in the hangar after everyone leaves for the evening! It takes concentration, focus, mind bending to be honest. Levitation is after all, in the end, just light hearted honesty. I practiced until it was second nature, almost a first impulse. I became the "night noise" in the big biplane ride hangar, inexplicable to all except the friendly mice who watched with great curiosity.

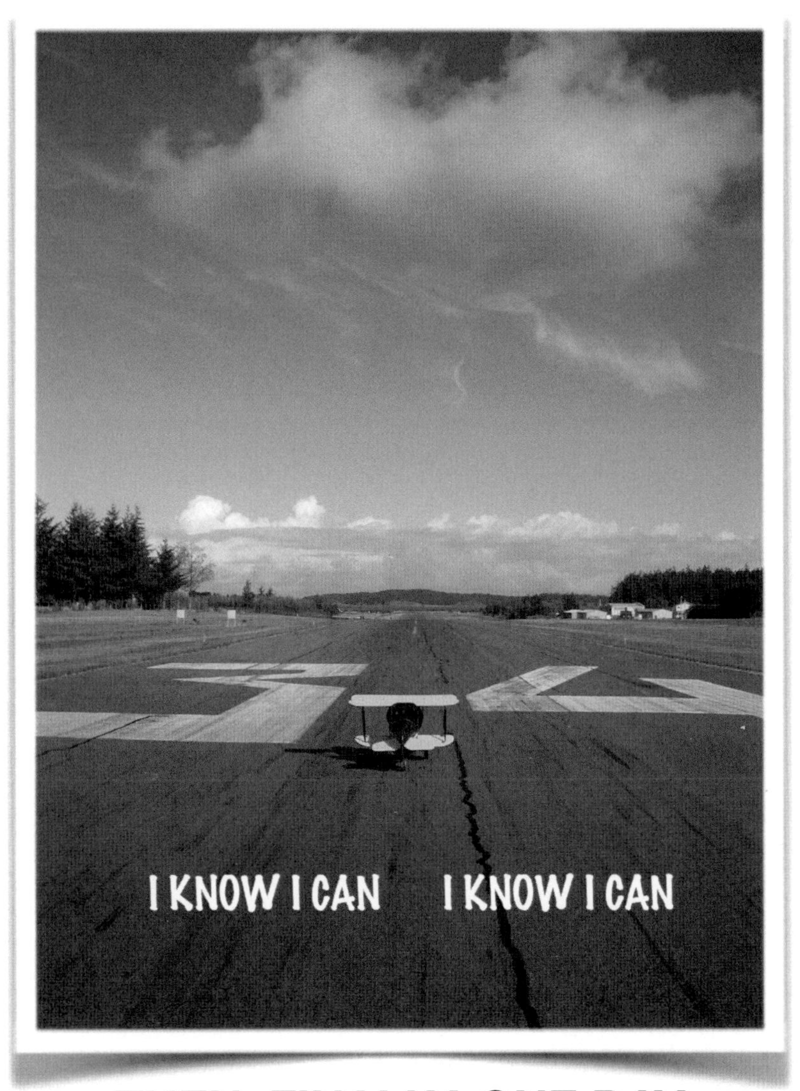

THEN, FINALLY, ONE DAY

WHEN NO ONE ELSE WAS FLYING

September 11, 2001

CASCADE LAKE

It is good to rest, to find a bit of water, some children, and listen to nothing but my heartbeat. To listen to internal echoes of chaos and complexity dancing. Rising up from this welter of thought, like flies straining against clear glass, is the notion of "more." Other worlds, places. Shards of time cut away from lives like pieces of sliced bell pepper. In the hangar I have listened to pilots talk of giant metal airplanes and magnificent adventures. Times when they felt almost *more* than alive.

I am more than curious AND there is time today. To go anywhere, wherever these mighty aircraft might be...the Woolly Beyond... Mother cautioned only that I be home before dark. I am not, I reason, confined to my island, or even to this space-time. Secretly, I have been waiting, anxious for this moment, to use the soft yellow button at the top of my control stick...which is indeed a tricky control. Children press it and we are suddenly in the most remarkable places, designs purely of imagination. I grin. Now it is my turn to squeeze my magical "goto" button and be Gulliver to *my* wishes. I hear a faint, momentary, cosmic chuckle.

I close my imaginary throttle and slide into a slice of quiet here beside the lake. In the still waters I see a rainbow, his eye catching mine.

YOUNG LAD

He didn't say much. Just looked me over carefully. Shy really. I sat quietly, soaking up the sun, waiting for his touch.

His parents were off nearby, and he had discovered me here by himself. There were no signs or warnings on me. No one to say, "Don't touch!"

He ran his hand across my port wing, and bent over to peer into the cockpit. Put his hand on the control stick and realized it moved! He could hear the clanking of the tail wheel turning as he gently pushed on my heart.

It wasn't long and we were a pair. Just the two of us. Sitting there on the point. His feet on the pedals, hand on the stick. Both of us dreaming of flying. Playing among the clouds.

ISLAND MARKET

Some people call their cars "island beaters." Leave keys in the ignition and spend 30 minutes in the produce section trading news and guffaws. In the Deli the tables are small and the seats too tight but the pilots are used to tight quarters and squatter's rights are part of their aerial and aural legacy here, at 2pm. The grizzled truck owner mused, "Used to be you knew everyone here, all the check out gals, the stockers. Took 2 years to learn where everything was after they closed the old Templins General store.

Easier to park now though and the grocery carts are full size. But the Famous Amos cookies are gone."

When things change, seem to become more efficient, easier to get, and look more alike - that's when my "elephant ear wing" technology, which performs just fine 80 years after it was invented - that's when all the modern gee-whiz hoopla goes kinda flat for me, and my Mom... We play in a sky Timeless and Perfect.

CROW VALLEY

Grass! The luxurious green of it. And pond! Geese all around. Barn. Chicago Aermotor windmill.

A valley called Crow.

Ohhhhh I could love this forever.

Fescue beneath my wheels. A short runway is all I would need, and permission from a friendly farmer….Come here often to bask in the glory of it all!

WATCH OUT

Kids know they are about to do ground loops and you gotta shout and clear the area. Pedal fast, hold the stick hard over and I, Little Magic, will make your head spin. Pedal fast enough and you may drag a wing tip… had it happen many times. Flags flying, faces shocked, but it is sooOOO much fun. Squeals of delight!

FedEx
Little Magic

THE POINT AT ROSARIO

Three thousand years ago people spent their days here fishing for salmon. Today, four thousand plus people live on the island, fishing for words to smooth the rough edges of life.

They name the trees and the plants, even the clouds that roll by. At night now, across a star packed heaven bright satellites sail by.

Disconnected from America by only the sea, the inhabitants savor what is left of living, parcel by parcel, scattered over 52 square miles. They notch the passage of time by limbic means, new buds on the pine tree, lupine shooting blue into April, yellow jackets swarming over picnic lunch every summer.

Sometimes it helps to have our names for things… but times like this, all I need is before me…Nameless and Unchanging….I am learning.

TOY PLANE CONFERENCE

We are all friends. They sit on the table at the back of the hangar, awaiting eager hands to lift them aloft and land them on the hangar concrete. One was once a hood ornament, another folds her die cast wings, the yellow German Eindecker hung in a minister's library ~~~Oh my, do we have stories to tell, sacraments of LOVE to share. It matters not our size. In our world of flight, we cherish our moments aloft!

CROW VALLEY POTTERY

Hidden roadside treasures here. People make things from earth! Draw it up from ground zero, spin it fire it and set it free for all to see.

Lanterns and metal work rusting - water dripping from plate to plate. They call it a water feature.

And a log cabin, chinked and weathered beyond description. As old as Methuselah.

I hear the sound of children now, laughing 100 years ago, and the beat of horses galloping past.

An echo, the soothing sound of a potters wheel, LOVE woven through fingers turning stardust clay to visual perfection.

JOHN DEERE

I remember Mother Magic admitted she loved the sound of someone by that name, next farm over in Almelund, Minnesota. She could hear him chugging ahead of the cultivator.

I love the colors. Honest green and in your eye yellow. Running a log splitter here.

By winter the wood will be ready. Unlock the energy of the sun from the last 100 years. Split and stacked. Smells terrific in this open air and crackling in a wood stove.

It's only April and we're thinking December, working sunshine into the mists of winter.

ORCAS HOTEL

I watch the people sitting on the front porch of the Orcas Hotel in the white wicker chairs. Their eyes are focused peacefully on the blue green sea and emerald islands. Gazing in the direction of home: big cities, traffic, and ordinary life. To which they know they must return. From somewhere in the heart comes a foreign but irresistible impulse - call the boss and say, “I’m not coming back!”

Home *is* this island they LOVE! They can contour the rest of their lives around the vagaries of salt wind and terrible AM radio reception. Sacrifice urgency for the completion of days strung together with sunrise mountain hikes and sunset fired cumulus spread over Canada. I have learned the pages of life are blank... Fill them with LOVE

THE VIMY

Vimy lands on Orcas! Her tales are remarkable. All across Africa, Australia and nonstop across the Atlantic in 1919! Lordy!... Mom and I have been content to explore the San Juan Islands. My dreams go into overdrive, and then mother Magic whispers to me, "Crete to Cape?" She hints of a possible future for her?… I spend the night combing internet destinations adrift in quantum entanglement dreams.

A YOUNG MERRILL WIEN

"BORN TO FLY"

MYSTICAL BEACH

Why would anyone live in a tenement building when… they could live mystically by the sea?

I knew an answer before I finished the thought. The mystery of flight is not that we *can* fly. It is rather, why we don't *always* fly. Not just on airliners, or in biplanes or Piper Cubs. In our dreams!

The freedom to practice perfection has no limits in time or place. Tenement or Sky. A grill chef at Reds Java House on a San Francisco wharf is the greasy perfect equal of the high stakes mutual fund administrator standing by his window in the Transamerica Pyramid.

I have chosen the Sky to manage *my* wealth. Measure cloud and wind and season to taste. Pepper with wonder. I can fly and never drop a bomb. Others may choose to live in a ghetto and never leave.

Free on the streets or free on the wind. Pure choice
This beach here... its almost too easy to be mystical.
The city? The beehive. Tougher I suppose.... Will I
remember this lesson tomorrow?

ROSARIO TERRIER

So the black terrier and I have this little talk. And he tells me how great his nose is. Likes to put it out in the wind, sometimes through an open car window. "Tells me everythhing I need to know," he brags.

"Oh, I know what you mean" I add, "I like to point my nose into the wind too…Especially landing!

"My biggest problem in life?" he asks, "I can’t stop chasing balls. A master throws a ball, I’m running!"

"Bigger problem here," I laugh. "Master throws a sky full of cu's, I'm dreaming; I'm at the takeoff end of a pasture in an instant!"

There is lull in our conversation. The scent of of spring on the island overwhelms. Luxuriant alchemy of grass, sal air, tapesty sky, marina boats rocking behind us. Breakfast aromas from the cafe. Sun bleaching our backs.

"What has the wind told you today?" I ask him, my aileron twisting to catch more sun.

"See that master reading her Sunday paper?…no need to worry about war in far off Pakistan. There is peace here, all around. Children laughing, balls to catch, clouds to chase."

I thought a moment. "True everywhere. Paoli PA. or Porto, Portugal. Evey moment. Any age."

The terrier smiled, "And certainly in every Northwest Spring that has ever been."

We celebrated the decision, pointing our noses into the wind

RAIN SHADOW

It rained. The Great Lakes biplane parked here left me this gift. I can see the sweep of the top wing almost. We spoke of summers past and lives lived.

Vietnam for his pilot, saving lives behind a round engined Air Force AD Skyraider. In the same war, Mother Magic's pilot flew a Navy Skyhawk jet. Both names began with "Sky" and it was to the sky that both were committed. To fly. To join up in formation now, open cockpit to open cockpit. Wave, break away in a sweeping arabesque and *FLY* some more. Always some more.

That speck on the horizon… a Biplane! "You up Magic?" Join up. Dance through the sky as if time has magically disappeared. Land. Sit in the hangar, talk, remember, and listen. To rain on corrugated roof.

Depart… leave a rain shadow of Perfection

PIKE PLACE

Yes, my ***first*** "off island flight!"

Me, a tiny biplane in a *big* Seattle. More than a little lost amid vertical concrete, mortar and brick. A kind of commerce meadow. But there are characters and children here and there must certainly be dreams. Curious eyes swimming beyond pools of cobblestone and curb. Cut flowers solemnly beg passers-by one last chance to blaze nature's glory.

Perhaps with dinner guests in candle-lit walk-ups, or to sit on a sunny kitchen window sill above a sink of morning dishes.

The long stem roses close by ask about fields in the sky, and if beyond the horizon there is a Master Rose which blooms forever?

I am just a little biplane and to me roses are very advanced. So I am puzzled, but I answer from my heart. "Fields of clouds are everywhere and ever changing, swept by cosmic wind and sparkling rain, drenched in sunshine, for the simple purpose of Rose, to be here, this moment, radiant and aware."

"Well then, are you free of space-time with your tiny wings, Little Magic?" they ask in hushed tones.

"As free as your fragrant petals have always been to fly across the canvas of continents."

"Would you lash us to your wings Little Magic, so we could touch this eternal wind?"

"Not necessary Dear Roses. That wind, LOVE, is in us this moment, in all the spaces between our doubts, Waiting."

I might have cried for my friends the roses, snipped and trimmed on a Seattle sidewalk, but, for me, they were beautiful today and would be again. I knew it certain.

Lessons come free on the streets and free on the wind.

KAYBEE TOYS

My goodness! I had no idea such heavens existed. A child's and a little biplane's paradise. Oh boy! Ohhboy! Oh boy!

I want to be an "action toy." Does it mean I have to learn to shoot a gun? Ummm? Hey, look at the Barbie dolls. Spinning tops, yo-yo's, and dominoes. We could fill the hangar with toys, wooden like me and Mom. Radio Flyer wagons and toboggans. Metal die-cast airplanes and Matchbox cars and trucks. Hotwheels and radio controlled gliders.

From the back of the store I hear a barbershop quartet of frogs serenading a shelf of Raggedy-Ann's with a beautiful Irish love song. All the dolls and toy soldiers bend their ears to listen. What a grand and glorious heaven this is. Does "grow up" mean no more real toys, no idle moments to play train or scrabble, or dig in the dirt with a steam shovel? To not sing my heart out just to be sweet to another soul?

I want part of me to grow up. My wings! To carry me through the cities of cloud that pass my way in life, to *PLAY* in the miraculous toy store called Planet Earth and Sky.

A Barbie dressed to the nines whispers she would love to fly with me, be a wing walker. I assure her she is free to choose that, but tease her she must have sawdust for brains.

"No high heels allowed!" I advise.

She kicks them off, high across the aisle.

"Oh my!"

ORCAS ISLAND
BIPLANE WORKS
XING
ORCAS

B-52

Warbird. Fortress. Gentle ugly. I felt a tremor wrinkle through me. In a baritone voice resonating the length of his fuselage, the battered warrior spoke to me.

"You may ask, young one, is my heart aflame with passion for the humanity dead in my shadows passing? The dark hail of iron pregnant with TNT..." His voice trails off skyward.

"I cannot imagine the pain in your soul," I mutter, wings drooping.

"Little Magic... dear little one - the world is not clean shaven after a hot shower. Men of the world do not sprinkle baby powder to hide the rashness of their work or words. For them, there is power in the idea of 'oblivion'- it drives their 'becoming.' I am the product of a lonely drafting board. A delivery system only. I have no heart or soul, or so they believe."

"You are sad, Mister Fortress, but cannot cry."

"My tears would only be mistaken for fuel leaks." I saw the sheen of JP4 on a nearby puddle.

"Raise me pilots who love the children of the world as you do Little Magic."

I promised solemnly I would.

We sat together a long time, silent, huddled wing under wing, and watched the sky spill cumulus tears across the cold tarmac

MUSEUM OF FLIGHT

The Cougar, the Cub and the Blue Angel pulled me aside. The Skyhawk spoke for them.

"Little Magic, if you choose to grow up you will be caught in a whirlwind of uncertainties. A freight load of gray legality, speed traps, wars, accounting irregularities, moral imperatives, poetic justice, road rage and media hype. The raw tonnage of experience can destroy your dreams, throw grit in your gears. When you make your 'final glide,' you will look behind and the story of your hours will be writ all around your wingtips, vaporous as the empty, cavernous sky. Your contrails gone, others left to pull their own now, dust devil to raincloud, your living will be scattered completely. A word here, a black rubber tire mark on a runway there. You may crawl into the corner of a barn and let the icicles of winter encase your lofty dreams. Or you can wander among the flowering fields of eternal Springs. Nurture your soul of wood and wire with simple sunshine by day, starlight by night.

"It has always been a lonely choice Little Magic. Be part of civilization's exams or a tourist across a timescape of your design. Linear, digital, analog, holographic, choose your quantum entanglement. Pass through earth and its granite lessons with the elan of a neutrino. Sweep off the porch, dangle your toes in the lake, savor onions grilling in your skillet. Gulp with prop and carburetor a firehose of oxygen. But *POINT* your nose into the wind for takeoff. And *FLY* Little Magic.

JUST FLY!

"Everyday a new lesson, Mom."

"Little Magic, you are becoming a true biplane."

MR PATTON

Who has let you wither away like this?" I whisper to Mr. Patton. His name on his nose.

"Father Time and Mother Earth mostly," he sighs. "I've had many good crews in my career, and the grass delights me here!" he says with a sparkle.

"And where have you flown over the years?"

"Oh my," he rumbles proudly, "I have been to all the Bees! And some Cees."

"Bees?" I scrunch up my leading edge with perplexion. Yes, perplexion!

"Berlin, Burma, Baton Rouge, Boston, Beijing. All the big Bees. You name a Bee, I've been there," he boasts.

I chime in, "Still working on the Cees I guess?

"Ah, the Cees," he paused, "they're tougher to log, further apart, hotter too. Calcutta, Cairo, Constantinople. I'm definitely a Bee airplane. Real proud of my Bees." There is a tiny twitch in his rudder, an exclamation point.

I congratulated Mr. Patton on his treasure of Bees and wished him more Cees, little Cees and cooler Cees, like Clover Bottom, Kentucky. He liked my joke.

As we parted, I began to wonder, would I let a letter of the alphabet become my life? What magical places of the heart would I chronicle with a simple logbook entry, 'another Bee'?

MT. CONSTITUTION 2409'

High Places! I want to make a covenant with them. Share them with anyone willing to risk the rust of old dreams to the cleansing power of the air. Strip away the lonely toilings of freeways and dark shrouded taverns. Life shackles grown over with old bark-skin like iron chains on tree limbs.

In the distance, Mt. Baker, curator of clouds for the North Cascades. One day I will fly over her. Cold and mute in the crystal air. I will tell her how I have loved her from afar - uncertain - if I scale her ramparts would her winds steal my soul? One day I will fly, fly beyond her reach, and answer my heart.

It will be the first of many granite conversations where the mountains speak of timelessness and I soak in the icy rarified dreams of worlds beyond their highest reaches.

THE OLGA STORE

Few folks come here now, off the main road just past the more famous Olga Artworks. Like a lot things in life, the store has a history that most have forgotten. Old 1929 biplanes get restored, pedal planes too that look old. And one day they will restore the Olga Store. People will come in to think about things they never knew but want to somehow remember, *now*.

One

AIR FORCE ONE

Air Force One winks an eyebrow window.

"They have told many secrets inside me, Little Magic, I carry them etched forever across my wing spars. They were old men who led the world, but sometimes misled the troops. Presidents and Secretaries of State. To China and Europe. All points between. Top secret missions and t-bone steaks, encoded radio transmissions, long starry nights sailing across 'fly-over' country."

"Who were they?" I ask.

"Ordinary people whose bar room banter seemed to become law when others listened. We use irreducible principles of physics to fly, Little Magic, and perhaps there are yet-to-be discovered laws of lift and drag that apply to human relations. They operate still with guesswork diplomacy and gunpowder."

"Must there be leaders?" I ask, thinking out loud

In a formation, there is always a leader. Geese have a lead in their 'V'."

"Ah," I said, "but what if there were no followers? Each of us would be our *OWN* leader!"

"My dear Little Magic," he sighed, "People fill the world with a tug of war between love and hate and then trust their lives to old men arguing in jets high above our magnificent planet where boundaries cease to exist. Pretty silly."

I agreed. "I am learning," I whispered quietly.

"My dear Little Magic," he sighed, "People fill the world with a tug of war between love and hate and then trust their lives to old men arguing in jets high above our magnificent planet where boundaries cease to exist. Pretty silly."

I agreed. "I am learning" I whispered quietly.

747

I hear music echoing inside. A symphony from the Acropolis, celebrating Icarus and Bernoulli. There is a crescendo from ancient wings, fluttering, breathing life into the soul of humanity, sweeping across a blue Aegean to every marsh and bay humanity calls home.

I am shocked. Such power in the meter and refrain. The volume rises until the ground beneath us trembles. Her rivets quiver with delight, as do mine.

"Where, Miss Zero 8 Hotel, where does the music begin?" I quiz her.

In character borne by the free winds of upper altitudes, Miss Zero 8 Hotel kneels beside me and nose to radome, whispers warmly, "Little Magic, it is the music of the spheres. We are its instruments. Flying wires to vortex generators, we sing the songs a world wishes to hear. Freedom for the heart."

She stood tall and proud, shining brightly in the sun.

And I heard in my own heart a new song.

4th OF JULY PARADE

Loaded up and headed to the big Parade. Me and my friends in the Puppy. Every year we look forward to this day. Big cheering crowds, young pedal plane pilots anxious with parents trailing close behind in case they panic. They rarely do though. Magic's pilot walks in front, his boombox playing "Those Magnificent Men in their Flying Machines." He gives a signal to me in the lead and the pilot speeds up then spins us on a dime, the crowd roars its approval as the announcers Ken and Karen Speck boom above the roar that we have been part of the parade for 20-some years! Makes me happy to be here on my island, home to something uniquely small town America. Fireworks tonight will echo through the hangar while my friends and I talk. You could live your whole life somewhere else and never know how **Perfect** a big parade on a small island is!

RED BARO
HARDW
RED BA

BARN AND SHADOW

I am too nosy. I tiptoe up to an old barn, a dairy parlor topped by hayloft, pasture stretching horizon bound. What will I find in the filtered light and shadows? A vision of farmer, a pilot, the clank of stanchions, the sweet fragrance of old manure? I have a sense, a warm abiding feeling, I am cared for, watched over. Sometimes I feel it in the tiny hands and feet that pedal me around the hangar at home. And then, there are stark moments like this, now, as if there is a Master Pilot, a guiding presence just beyond my outstretched wings. Visible or not, palpable.

Mother Magic's words ring true. Stop. Look and Listen. I can trust. I can learn. I can play at living with all the energy at my command. Toss my soul among the clouds of a thousand lifetimes and experience the Joy that awaits, patient as clover, ever green... Never too late, either, to thank this barn for being here, now, this very moment.

TALL OAK GIFTS

She sits on a hill overlooking the airport. Has watched it grow from pasture to pavement, heard the cough of Cub engines on cold Fall mornings turn to occasional whistle of corporate jets.

"I have a gift for you Little Magic. It is a sea of crunch gold. Leaves which have cleaned your sky and captured the rain, offered you shade on a summer afternoon. They have made a final flight, realized their well understood dream: To twirl and soar in ever so brief a passage from limb to earth. They have only one flight to make in life, and each does it perfectly."

As if on cue, a wintery wind kicks up and fills my cockpit with leafy gold... Today I feel wealthy in ways which matter most… I have many flights to make, one life to perfect.

BEAR

I love the biplane hangar. No matter where I travel now, I always come Home. Mr. Bear only visits now and then. Everyone knows there are no bears on Orcas, or poisonous snakes. But, there he is!

"Are you comfortable Mr. Bear?" I ask. If he is I know I can get close. He smiles, the sunshine warming his spirit and genteel bearishness. In a bearitone voice he asks, "Little Magic, I hear from your little friends in the hangar you have been off island, to America! Is it scary?"

How can I tell him that only he can decide that? I answer, "Sometimes on the way to what's supposed to happen something much better happens. America has struck me as an extraordinary tableau of time and distance, here and there a quiet place or a prettier street than ordinary, yet all the while a tsunami of LOVE lies undiscovered around the next bend." Somehow I am sure he already knew that. He was just testing me...

I learn quickly sometimes. I think

WEST SOUND

A Cub Scout meeting, island style.

The beach rocks are mostly round. “Not the best skippers,” I hear one confess.

“Hey, I found a great one,” someone yells.
A scrap of driftwood too, for the dog to fetch. Where there is sunshine, salt water, a rocky beach with a selection of skipper stones to throw, children are happy. Rearranging the order of rocks and things with a symphony of “kerplunks.”

I will bring my pedal plane friends *here* to rearrange the mysteries of life.

We can try to ‘kerplunk’ a few of life’s ‘mysteries’ once and for all!

EASTSOUND PARK

At sunrise I sit at the water's edge. The world divides itself and my thoughts plunge into an unknown abyss. We know nearly everything about land yet almost nothing about the vast seas covering seventy percent of the earth. How can that be?

We walked the earth first then set sail upon her seas. We joined the sky on fabric covered wings, yet even in our most sturdy submarine, barely go below the surface of the oceans. Man and pedal planes will

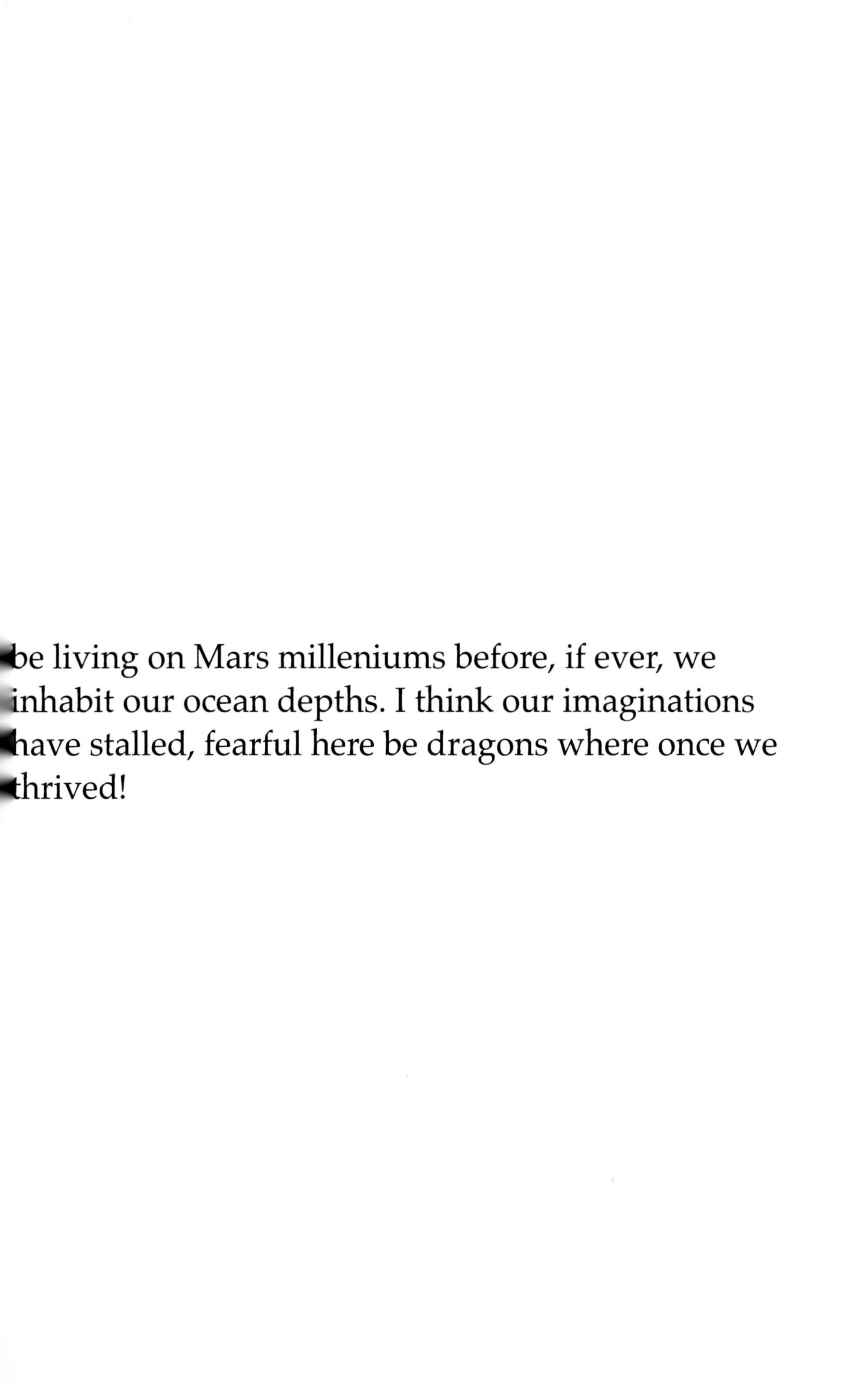

be living on Mars milleniums before, if ever, we inhabit our ocean depths. I think our imaginations have stalled, fearful here be dragons where once we thrived!

YELLOW ISLAND

I am hiding in a sea of color. Up to my wings in splendor. Knotted and tickled by runners of green around my axles - imprisoned in a fragile beauty, intoxicated by an ancient perfume.

I cannot even speak of the Joy here. Mother would think I have gone mad.

I imagine for a moment a vaulted sky, sapphire blue. Summer cumulus packed like snow cones one upon the other. Each a color of the rainbow. Racing before an August wind into a late and sculpted sunset. To reappear in morning mist teasing the early light. In the palette of quiet here, I measure the stock of my life to come, and choose among infinite paths - one.

LOVE.

With my friends in the sky.

WINDSONG

Lovely afternoon grass. Encroaching on the open spaces between cathedrals douglas fir. Kim and her dog Maggie, forgetting morning and welcoming April afternoon. Peaceful here. The clarity. Blur of Maggie chasing instinct on billiard green earth. Oiled hinges yet creaking. Wooden swing content to rock the heart of any soul wise enough to sit awhile. Just sit. And swing.

Into summer. Into *forever.*

ORCAS ISLAND
BIPLANE WORKS
XING
109

FOWLERS CORNER

Plum tree or daffodils. Quiet among the growing planetarium stars.

Three way road intersection here. Three sheep thirty yards away, safe behind a three-wire fence, baffled by a red and yellow biplane in their midst.

We talk. Between bites.

They are really more interested in eating.

"So, you can really fly?" they ask.

"Yes!"

"But why?" all three ask in unison.

"To play among the clouds." I point with my wing tip in the direction of up.

"Is it not cold, *UP* there?"

"Not with nice wool sweaters, or sheepskin ackets."

The daffodils are laughing, but the sheep are ıot.

FAMILIES

Every summer they came back. Every year I looked forward to seeing them. So where does family begin?

Is it like Matt's Chamber Music, his concerts which flow from one performance into the next? Each member with a part to play… Family is everything on this earth to me. It is LOVE lived. The years are never so long or the days so short you cannot LOVE each other in the moment. Each of us is playing an instrument in the harmony which LOVE has written on every page of music, every moment of our lives.

Thank you Matt, Adam, Charlotte and Kenny. From pedals to tail feathers, I welcome your Smiles forever.

WORDS FAIL

....

.... !

Its OK. Just enjoy the view…

Like I did.

Some of the best learning comes quietly.

So……quiet…

GLIDER

Miss Glider sizes me up. She was once towed aloft behind a biplane, remembers it well.

"How do you fly Little Magic," she quizzes me.

"The same way you do Miss G. With invisible lift, circling in imagination like you do in a thermal." She looks at me again, still somewhat puzzled, "Are you for real?" she asks.

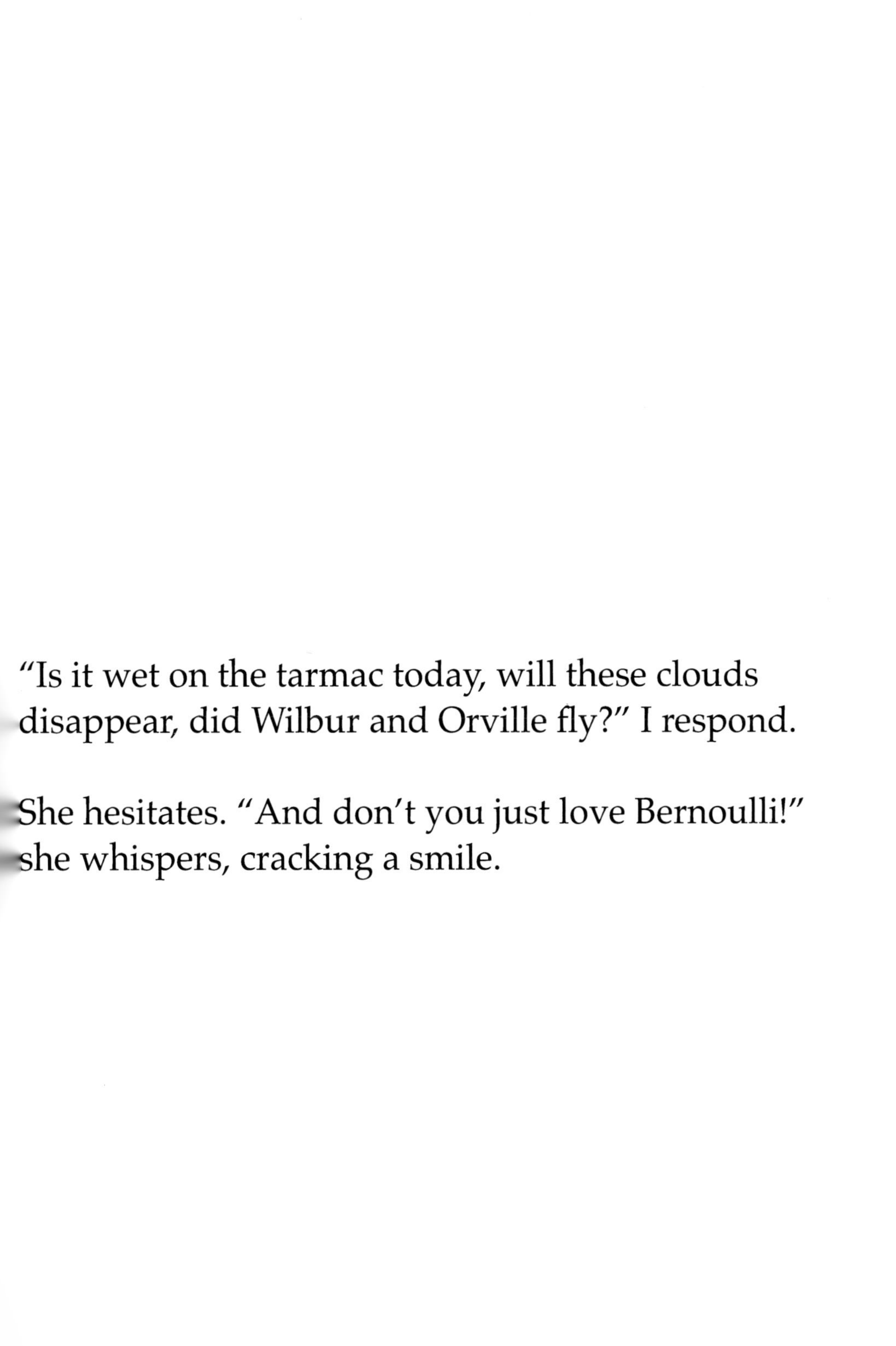

"Is it wet on the tarmac today, will these clouds disappear, did Wilbur and Orville fly?" I respond.

She hesitates. "And don't you just love Bernoulli!" she whispers, cracking a smile.

PUTTING GREEN

Perfect green here. Rolling, sloping. Like life. I want every landing to be perfect. Golfers want every putt to go in. Few landings are perfect. Yet a lifetime of golf will yield a few perfect putts. Life is one day, one putt, one flight at a time. LOVE holds the control stick or the putter with Patience, awaiting the moment of *our* decision. I choose to Fly. LOVE navigates life for me. (The old barn is Smiling).

QUICKIE

"Yes I know I look weird Little Magic, like a cross between a biplane and a pylon racer."

"That's Ok Miss Quickie, you're B U tiful, *and* you can FLY!"

"Why Thank You Little Magic. Wanna fly some formation sometime?"

"Throw me in that wild cerulean blue any day!"

HAY FIELD

I see people sitting on hay bales at the Fly-In, and this field is right next to my hangar. Now I know what a hay bale feels like. There, answered my own question! And it seems to me, I should try to answer as many of my *own* questions as I can in this lifetime. Lots of people have answers, and I can read or listen to them. Works for them but I have to find what works for me. Answer my own questions the best way I know how…

Can be kinda itchy sometimes.

PAPER AIRPLANE CONTEST

With a strong arm, the paper airplane will sail above the gym floor, and hang suspended in midair, like the hopes and dreams of its pilot.

A journey of moments, a flight of mere seconds, may lead to a lifetime of joy.

With a strong heart the boy can choose. A necklace of shining moments, brief flights one beside the other, strung together to form a lifetime.

A solar wind may power his spacecraft to galaxies "Vikings" never imagined.

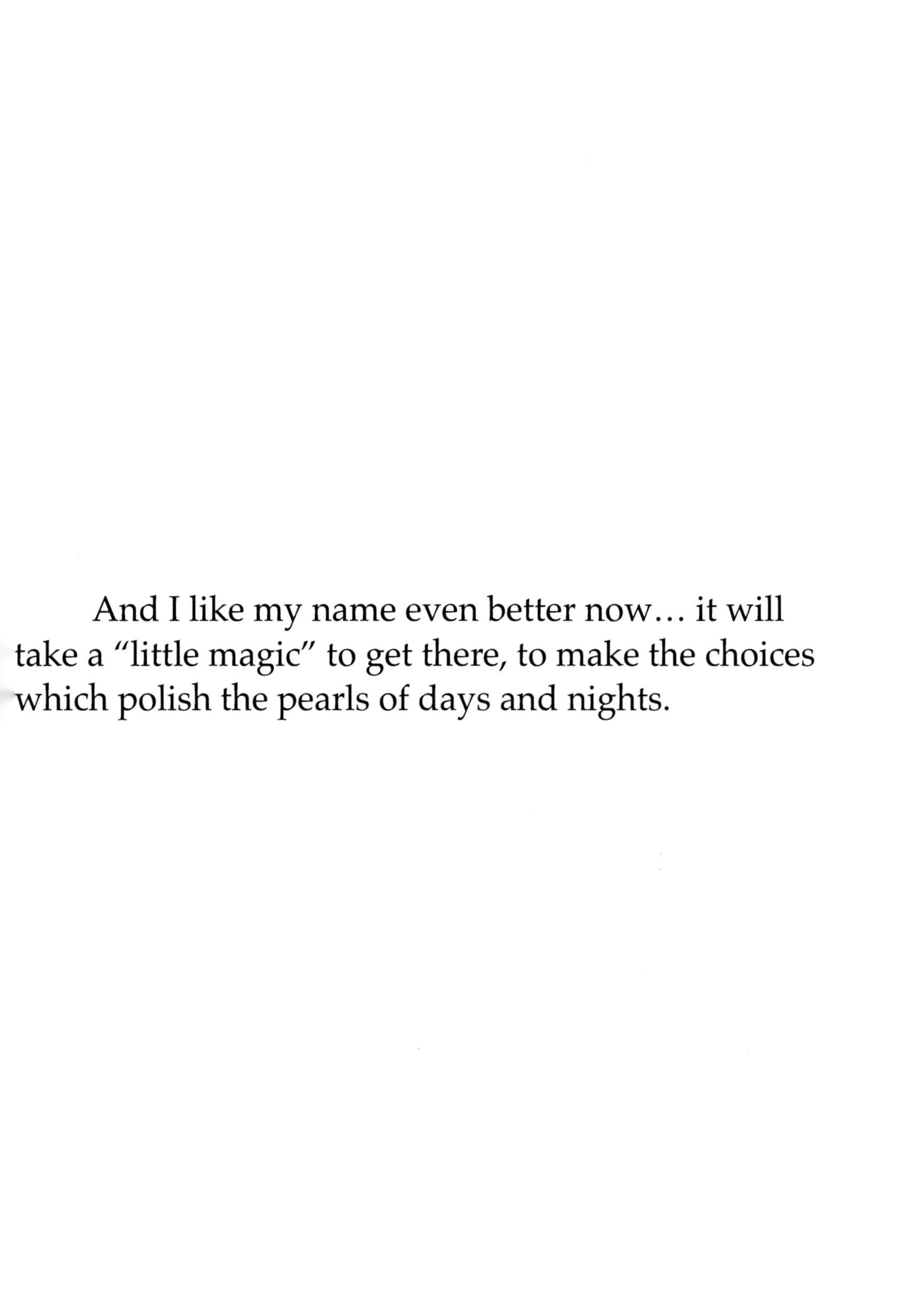

And I like my name even better now… it will take a "little magic" to get there, to make the choices which polish the pearls of days and nights.

CASCADE LAKE WINTER

Peaceful, cold, beautiful to behold. It is so simple really. I fly with the seasons, which will entertain forever one after another. I yield to their evanescent presence, hot or cold, promise or purpose…

I am learning to LOVE
4th of July! or 4th of January!

LOVE
AND THEN.
RED BARON

...listen for the Cosmic Chuckle
ORCAS

MY HANGAR MY HOME

I love my Mom.
I love my Hangar.
I love my Home.

I may travel the world, even beyond, but Home is where my heart is. Anyone can see why. Look at the all the smiles, the quiet evenings, the color and nonsense on the walls. I have often watched my mother from across the field, unbeknownst to her.

We are the best of friends. She is so patient with me, with her pilot, with the years, even the oil and brake changes.

We share a lifetime of Joy!

1000 YEARS FROM NOW

How did we, all of us, get there from here? Did we fall down a black hole? Did the weight of all the souls of all time add up and overflow the well of life? Was there a limit to the number of times we could not get it right? Did we prove or disprove the existence of infinite paths to the Creator? Did ants and insects evade the power law?

We made it through. Not as bystanders to our fate, but as arbiters of it. There were no credit cards to charge goodwill and then declare bankruptcy when it was time to pay it back. Some called it Karma. The clearing view of the path ahead lay among the stars and galaxies which were now ours to infinitely explore. A thousand years from now became a single grain of time. Beauty and speed were not things to parade on a fashion runway in high heels or on glimmering cars plastered with words.

In the Smile of another we linked ourselves to the wings of Forever. If there was ever a thought of separation from our Forever, it was lost in the Joy of knowing it had never been possible. In the universe of all probable futures, mankind and pedal planes chose rainbows, biplanes, occasional shade. ... And **LOVE!**

SMALL LIES, SIMPLE JOYS, OCCASIONAL TRUTHS

WHERE YOU BEEN BOY...A LOVE Story..Amazon

THEN A MIRACLE is on Amazon.

BORN TO FLY by Merrill Wien is on Amazon

For biplane rides on Orcas Island:
https://www.orcasbiplanerides.com/

For biplane rides in Magic One, now in Chino, CA:
https://barnstormersbiplanerides.com/

iwillneverbeinanuclearwar.com

littlemagic.com

alittlemagic@gmail.com

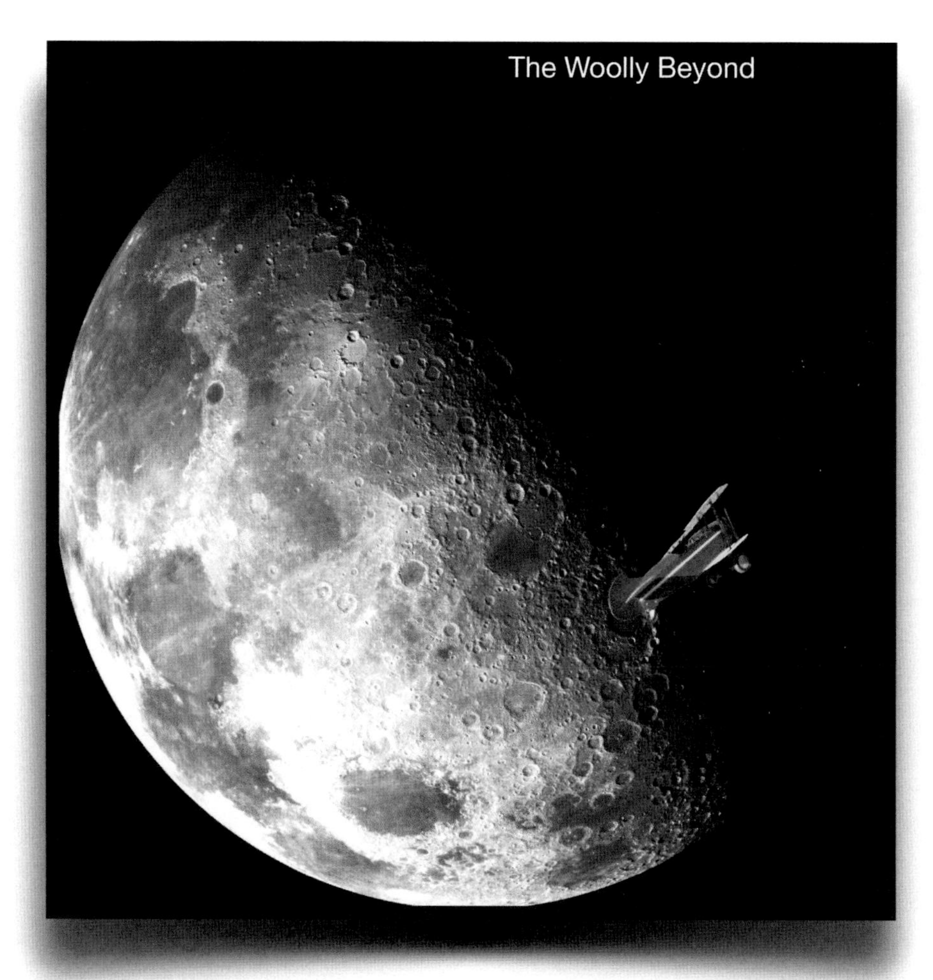

**Feel welcome to write a review on Amazon.
It helps Little Magic
fly to the Woolly Beyond.**

Made in the USA
Coppell, TX
31 August 2020

35035658R00064